FROM WALES

Edited by Simon Harwin

First published in Great Britain in 2000 by
YOUNG WRITERS
Remus House,
Coltsfoot Drive,
Woodston,
Peterborough, PE2 9JX
Telephone (01733) 890066

HB ISBN 0 75431 735 8
SB ISBN 0 75431 736 6

FOREWORD

This year, for the first time ever, Young Writers proudly presents a showcase of the best mini sagas from over 2,500 up-and-coming writers nationwide.

To write a mini saga - a story told in only fifty words - much imagination and skill is required. *Mini Sagas From Wales* achieves and excels these requirements and this exciting anthology will not disappoint the reader.

The thought, effect and hard work put into each mini saga impressed us all and the task of editing proved challenging due to the quality of entries received, but was nevertheless enjoyable. We hope you are as pleased as we are with the final selection and that you continue to enjoy *Mini Sagas From Wales* for many years to come.

CONTENTS

Hungry!	Rachel J Lee	1
Untitled	Roxanne Gilbert	2
The Black Figure	Sian Jones	3
Total Eclipse	Emma Griffiths	4
Red Is The Colour Of Blood	Imran Jina	5
Sports Day	Joshua Bradshaw	6
Broken Heart	Dana Louise Jones	7
First Day At School	Kelly Larcombe	8
My Holiday	Claire Howarth	9
Fire At Play	Laura Scott	10
My First Day Of School	Jenny Williams	11
The Gane	James Townsend	12
Round And Round	Louise Gabica	13
Hitting The Ball	Sarah Dymock	14
My First Day At School,	Shane Rutherford	15
The Best Meal Ever	Ceri James	16
Never Again	Lindsey Badham	17
SATs	Thea Harris	18
The Dream, The Reality	Jessica Carter-James	19
Breaking Bones	James Morgan	20
My Last Race	Thomas McVeigh	21
I Dived Deeper	Gemma Brittan	22
A Day At The Beach	Louis Barker	23
Flying	Hayley McCaughey	24
Easy Option	Simon Ellis-Williams	25
Wacky Wisdom	Patricia Faye Apsee	26
Crime Doesn't Pay	Ruth Fryzer	27
War	Andrew Bevan	28
When Everything Became Nothing	Katie Haines	29
Julius The Great	Kelly-Marie Jones	30
Nessie	Robert Shuker	31
The Monster	Hannah Walford	32
Once In A Lifetime	Aileen Powell	33

Dreams	Rosa Williams	34
Bill's Most Eventful Day	Max Rowe	35
Catch Me	Danielle Cox	36
The Chase	Rhyanon Griffiths	37
Impact	Frances Price	38
The Bee Sting	Leah Shoemake	39
Morning Call	Thomas James	40
Dogs	Darmasakthini Arujunan	41
At The Edge Of The Cliff	Victoria Sanders	42
The Total Eclipse	Nicola Tingle	43
Thank Goodness	Gemma Bubb	44
Untitled	Irene Davies	45
Spider In The Bath	Emma Jones	46
Under Pressure	Annabel Gaba	47
Evil Wears No Face . . .	Beth Winkworth	48
Tag!	Sarah Marie Jones	49
The Mexican Staring Frog	Alex Walpole	50
The Mermaid Purse	Sara Jones	51
The Race	Jamie Christy	52
The Monster	Angharad Heard	53
The Forest Of No Escape	Joanne Bamber	54
The Monster In My Closet	Emma Louise Thomas	55
No Way Out	Daniel O'Grady	56
Ready Or Not	Christine Vicary	57
Trial	Suraya Jina	58
Total Anticipation	Gregory Stevens	59
A Thousand Letters!	Abi Anderson	60
Short Change	Rhiannon Stanton	61
Train Traffic	Emily Edge	62
Nightmare	Rhiannon Walters	63
Now You See Me, Now You Don't	Cerys Stanton	64
Mini Saga`	Gareth Leech	65
The Bomb Squad	Dean Harris	66
Hide-And-Seek	Rosemary Jones	67
The Grave	Cheryl Davies	68
Black Cape Comes To Life	Rhian Thomas	69
Magic Circle	Emily Bethan Rees	70

I Saw It	Amy Barrett	71
The Shark	Angharad Rebecca Preston	72
Mad	Anna Blainey	73
The Cave?	Katherine Morgan	74
Survival By Chance	Philip Dawson	75
The Captive	Colette Morgan	76
Monster Cracker	Johanna Rafferty	77
The Attack	Bethan Lewis	78
The Thief	Saravanan Arujunan	79
The Element Of Surprise	Victoria Leonard	80
The Hunt	Rebecca Waite	81
Yesterday's Rubbish	Nicholas Like	82
Good Morning Playgroup!	Siân Harries	83
The Eclipse	Samantha Jones	84
Getting Ready	Darryl Ovenstone	85
Total Eclipse	Christina Evans	86
The Thing In A Hole	Kirsty Gould	87
Earthquake	Rebecca Anderson	88
The Chase	Sian Griffiths	89
The Things I'll Do For A Fiver	Siân Patrick	90
Aeroplane	Nicola Banner-Martin	91
Flying	Laurie Jones	92
Shakespeare In Love	Akosa Melifonwu	93
The New Visitor	Ryan Willetts	94
Darkness	Rachel Jarvis	95
When Darkness Fell	Rhys Nicholas	96
First Day	Sarah Lewis	97
Invalid	Joanne Dawkins	98
Death	Laura Wilce	99
A Shot At Me	Christopher Griffiths	100
The Dentist	Rebecca Charley	101
Lost In Space Forever	Lucy Fowler	102
Rugby	Tracy Thomas	103
Oh No Mum	Julia Sandberg	104
Cold Night	Daryl Goodwin	105
The Unwelcome Visitor	Sarah Harris	106
The Frightening	Rebecca Aplin	107

My Jungle	Dawn Elizabeth Emmerton	108
War Of Water	Michelle Langford	109
A Journey: C'est La Vie	Michael D Brown	110
Arachnophobia	Hannah Jenkins	111
The Fantasy	Robert Rees	112
The Headmaster's Office	Lara Davies	113
Operation: Entry	Michael Haddock	114
A Restless Night	Jodie Parfitt	115
Thunderstorm	Arshiya Mastan	116
The Midnight Scare	Jade Coulthard	117
The Envelope	Abi Edwards	118
The Urging Light	Simone Morris	119
Eclipse	Andrew Butler	120
The Lure	Bethan Jones	121
Creeping	Laura Burr	122
Sea Monster	Helen Webber	123
The Final Blow	Natasha White	124
Revenge	Hannah Davies	125
Buried Treasure	Ben Hebblewhite	126
11th Of August 1999, A Historic Day . . .	Dafydd Jones	127
The Black Monster	Christopher Williams	128
The Racing Pigeon	Emma O'Connell	129
The Moon That Needed A Friend	Moshudul Islam	130
The Stalker	Jade Wood	131
The First	Leanne Gardner	132
Time Is Precious	Charlotte Allen	133
Temptation	Manuela Solera-Deuchar	134
I Surrender	Rebecca Tudgay	135
Earth Wars	Shaun Jennings	136
Fear And Triumph	Becky Hammonds	137
Space - The One And Only Voyage To Mars	Rachael Fretwell	138
The Eclipse	Elinor Marsh	139
It Came And It Went	Andrea Roberts	140
Where's The Exit	Sarah Davies	141
Newcomer	Sam Brown	142

Silent Darkness	Nicole Bruton	143
The Trial	Sharon Davies	144
Diamond	Hannah Aylward	145
A Plot To Kill	Sara Brunt	146
The Tiger	Freya Michaud	147
The Nappy Argument	Katrina Sweetser-Hawkes	148
A Spooky Night	Phillip J Lewis	149
The Screaming Wolf	Ashley Bolwell	150
Hidden	Adele Watts	151
Time To Totality	Helen Jennifer Jones	152
My Mum	Nilesh Mepani	153
Nightmare!	Bernadette Lemon	154
The Gush In The Wind	Nick Taylor	155
Game Over	Derek Pang	156
The Eclipse	Clare Sim	157
The Important Document	Lowri Evans	158
A Golden Silence	Caroline McBurnie Jones	159
In The Middle Of The Night	Joanna Moore	160
Hilda's Big Trick	Kayleigh Baldwin	161
Oh! Brother	Emma Louise Bates	162
A Ray Of Light	Chantelle Thomas	163
Today's The Day!	Lucy Jayne Marsh	164
The Sorry Hunter	Lisa Francis	165
The Chase	Rhiannon Sheppard	166

The Mini Sagas

HUNGRY!

He stood, staring me squarely in the face.
His long slimy tongue hung between his enormous
white sharp teeth, desperate for food.
He paced around watching my every move as he
planned his attack.
The next thing I knew the cheeky dog was running
off with my sausage.

Rachel J Lee (12)

Untitled

Escalating up, the view around was breathtaking,
Until we reached the top, with no return,
The descending journey was upon us!
Everyone screaming with fear and joy,
Swaying back and forth, upside down,
Then a sudden *halt!*
Relief was felt from all aboard this rocking
Roller-coaster ride . . .

Roxanne Gilbert (10)

THE BLACK FIGURE!

As I woke up
and cried out for my mum
after my nice deep sleep
a big black figure stepped
into the room.

I screamed, I yelled
and as the curtains
were drawn back
I peeped out from my
warm yellow blanket
and saw

     My big sister!

Sian Jones (12)

TOTAL ECLIPSE

They gazed up to the sky as slowly, silently
the shadow crept forward.
The skies began to change from blue to grey
as the darkness began to fall.
A spooky feeling filled the air.
The crowds cheered, as the shadow slid away
to show a glowing sun once more.

Emma Griffiths (11)

RED IS THE COLOUR OF BLOOD

Knife poised in hand, the man tentatively chose his victim.
As the blade pierced the flesh a distinctive smell invaded my nostrils.
A red liquid seeped out as the serrated metal sliced the skin
on the opposite side.
My dad passed me a juicy slice of watermelon from his plate.

Imran Jina (12)

SPORTS DAY

I was lined up ready to race.
I heard the starting signal,
I started jumping in my sack.
I fell over before the halfway mark.
I kept jumping as hard as I could,
They were cheering me on as I got
closer to the finish.
I jumped, *I won!*

Joshua Bradshaw (10)

BROKEN HEART

My heart was pierced by an arrow.

I felt the pain through my body.

My stricken wounded soul,
Will my heart ever heal?

Friends crowded around my bedside
Waiting for my everlasting pain to end!

They wiped my tearful eyes,
A voice said
        'You'll get over him.'

Dana Louise Jones (12)

FIRST DAY AT SCHOOL

I went into my new classroom.
Fresh new books were on the shelf.
My new teacher walked in. She was tall.
She asked me a question and looked
at me like I was some sort of alien.
I slid down in my seat, not knowing
the answer.

Kelly Larcombe (10)

My Holiday

I was on my way to France on the ferry.
My tummy was rumbling.
I think it was all the excitement.
It was getting nearer and nearer
Then suddenly I could see something.
                              It was France!

Claire Howarth (10)

FIRE AT PLAY

Up they went, blasting in the dark moonlit sky
bursting with colours of energy
and glittering as they came down.
Then a pause . . .
suddenly the biggest bang was made and
shot up with loads of colours.
That was the end of the firework display!

Laura Scott

MY FIRST DAY OF SCHOOL

I was standing on the playground all alone.
I was just standing there waiting for
one of my friends to turn up.
I waited and heard a car.
I thought it was my friend but it wasn't.
Finally she came.

Jenny Williams (10)

THE GAME

We have just started the game of rugby against Tutshill
We move up the field passing the ball between us.
John takes the ball up and scores.
They have possession of the ball.
Mike tackles their player, he takes the ball and he scores.
Yippee! We won the game!

James Townsend (10)

ROUND AND ROUND

It's my turn. I've got the bat in my
hand and *whack!*
I'm running as fast as I can.
John's got the ball, he's
running to 4th base.
Can I get there in time?
Yes! I've scored a rounder.

Louise Gabica (10)

HITTING THE BALL

There I stood, the ball flying towards me
I swung my bat and *whoosh!*
I saw the ball fly across the field.
I ran as fast as my little legs could take me
To base, 1, 2, 3, and 4 . . . yes!
I had scored a rounder!

Sarah Dymock (10)

MY FIRST DAY AT SCHOOL

My first day at school I was frightened to death.
I thought I would never make a friend.
I just stood in the middle of the playground.
Then a boy came up to me and said
'Would you like to play football?'
After that I made lots more friends.

Shane Rutherford (10)

THE BEST MEAL EVER

There it was, chicken curry
and rice ready to be eaten.
Mum said 'Watch out, it's hot?
But I didn't care.
I put it into my mouth.
Yum! Yum! I said.
In twenty minutes it
was all eaten up.
Then my mum said
'Chips tomorrow,' and I said
'I can't wait!'

Ceri James (10)

NEVER AGAIN

The roller-coaster, the big sloppy, terrifying
roller-coaster, 100 miles per hour.
The icy wind slapping you in the face.
My brother shouting, my sister screaming
and me frozen. Not being able to say
anything, just staring at the somersaulting
track ahead, one thing is for sure
never again!

Lindsey Badham (10)

SATs

I was on the last question.
It was one hundred times one hundred.
It was so confusing, I couldn't understand.
My heart was pounding like a stampede
                             rushing towards me.
Ding! Ding! The bell went.
What's the answer?
Papers in please.
Oh yeah, ten thousand!

Thea Harris (10)

THE DREAM, THE REALITY

That night I dreamt that I was clearing the last fence,
that I had won, then I woke up,
I couldn't remember a thing,
all I knew was that I could win,
I would win.

Jessica Carter-James (10)

BREAKING BONES

I switched it on, it gave me the last chance to do this.
I walked to the edge. I jumped, I closed my eyes,
this time I made it. I was so thrilled something
gave me the urge to let go. I did, I fell about fifty feet.
Broken bones!

James Morgan (10)

MY LAST RACE

It was a very long race,
Who has the quickest car?
Who will win the race?
My heart was pounding,
I was only just winning.
My engine blew,
Three cars hit me.
Our cars were in flames
My race was over
I turned off my PlayStation.

Thomas McVeigh (10)

I DIVED DEEPER

I dived as I met the fierce eyes of a shark.
I tried to scream but the slapping fins of the fishes
were overtaking me. Bubbles rose to the surface.
I was trembling, my mum burst through the door,
panicking. 'What's wrong?'
I was relieved. I was dreaming.

Gemma Brittan (10)

A DAY AT THE BEACH

It was a sunny day and I was going to the beach.
I swam in the sea and played in the sand.
I made a sandcastle and collected some shells.
Then it rained so I had to go home.

Louis Barker (10)

FLYING

We were sitting ready to jet off to Portugal.
Excitement was building up in me.
All of a sudden we started moving.
The seat belt sign came on.
Before I knew it we were in mid air.
All of a sudden, bang! We hit the runway.
We are *here!*

Hayley McCaughey (10)

EASY OPTION

My accomplice was dead, the team was relying on me.
I got my 9mm silencer out. Seven bullets left,
at least ten of the enemy facing me. They fired,
I fired, seconds later I was out of ammo. Only one
thing left to do, *click!* I turned the PlayStation off.

Simon Ellis-Williams (10)

WACKY WISDOM

Ali sat down in the hard backbone chair 'So you really
predict the future?' questioned Ali.
'I wouldn't be here for a good laugh, dearie,' answered the old hag.
'Well tell me what will happen in five seconds.'
Holding a brick she said 'A brick will come.' *Bang!*

Patricia Faye Apsee (10)

CRIME DOESN'T PAY

Deftly he picks at the lock
Silently working to counteract the alarm,
The precious stone will be his,
No more worrying about where his next
Meal is coming from.
The large *gem* is at last his,
Quickly turning as he feels a hand on his
Shoulder,
'You're nicked my son.'

Ruth Fryzer (11)

WAR

My comrades and I stood proudly to attention,
uniforms gleaming. Soon we heard rumbling noises
which got nearer and louder. Afraid, we stood our
ground, then four of my friends fell. The grab
came down, my friends were swept aside and the
rest of us skittles stood to attention again.

Andrew Bevan (10)

WHEN EVERYTHING BECAME NOTHING

There it lay before me.
Its tongue flickered and its eyes sparkled.
It looked so confident as it slithered
along the ground towards me.
Fear flooded my heart.
My strengths became weaknesses,
love became hate and as I stood there
mesmerised, life became death.

Katie Haines (12)

JULIUS THE GREAT

The competition began between Julius
from Norway and Zorba from Greece.
The competition was to do something heroic.
Zorba ran towards the forgotten land
and Julius fought the cruellest monster alive,
but didn't return for days. When he did he
was wearing the monster's fur.
Zorba never returned!

Kelly-Marie Jones (13)

NESSIE

The monster's spiky back broke through the water.
A huge head appeared at their toes.
'It's real,' Paul said.
'Of course,' Nessie replied, 'come for a ride.'
Nervously the boys stepped onto the monster's back.
Whoosh! They glided through the water.
Better than jet skis.
'Bath's over,' said Mom.

Robert Shuker (10)

THE MONSTER

I heard it
That distinctive noise
That had terrified me for years.
The yellow and black monster
Speedily advanced on me.
The powerful body
Darted from side to side,
Choosing its next victim.
Suddenly pain hit me
Piercing my arm
Like a dagger.
'Someone kill the wasp!' I yelled.

Hannah Walford (13)

ONCE IN A LIFETIME

The light was disappearing and slowly
our world plunged into darkness.
I shivered as the air turned colder.
Our eyes were fired on the sky as the
sun was snatched from it.
Minutes went by and slowly the sun
began to return.
The crowd gasped.
The eclipse was over.

Aileen Powell (11)

DREAMS

I slowly drift away into a world
I've never explored before. It's new and exciting.

I see a door. I open it. Inside it's dark and gloomy.
I look around, exploring the room.

I hear a voice. I try to ignore it, but it gets louder.
'Wake up Eddie, breakfast.'

Rosa Williams (12)

BILL'S MOST EVENTFUL DAY

Bill was confused, cows were huddling
under the trees, people were putting
protective strips over their eyes,
the birds stopped singing. What was happening?
Then he understood, it was the end of the world.
Total darkness engulfed him.
Suddenly light and relief flooded over him,
it was only an eclipse.

Max Rowe (11)

CATCH ME

Through the uncut grass I ran
attempting to get away.

Behind me he panted as he tried
to catch me.

Over the river and past the orchard
I raced to get to my house, safety!

Finally I reached my doorstep, when
'Tag, you're it!' yelled my brother.

Danielle Cox (13)

THE CHASE

As I ran through the dark forest a
mysterious figure came nearer.
The heavy breathing got louder and louder.
I couldn't run or shout, there was too much
pressure.
He called *'Rhyanon . . .*
Rhyanon.'
Oh no! Can't get away, he's getting close
enough to grab me!
'Rhyanon, Rhyanon,
time for school.'

Rhyanon Griffiths (12)

IMPACT

Tension builds.
We begin our ascent,
The summit approaches.
I brace myself for the unknown!
Suddenly we gather speed
Pressure forces me downwards.
My head spins.
My stomach churns.
I cling to the bar, my only hope of survival.
The sensation continues forever . . .
Then silence . . .
'So which roller-coast is next?'

Frances Price (15)

THE BEE STING

The alarming noise suddenly became closer.
The sound was piercing my eardrums. My body
froze. There was a sudden silence. My heart
was beating vigorously. I started to perspire.
I felt *pain!* I screamed loudly, breaking any
silence! I was stung by a bee!

Leah Shoemake (13)

MORNING CALL

She spotted him. Then the noise began, a continuous barking.
She ran from the window to the door and back to the window to
check on his progress. As he got closer the noise got louder.
He reached the door and pushed the letters through.

'Mum, the post has come.'

Thomas James (12)

DOGS

We heard howls of vicious dogs in the
distance! We had to escape! Suddenly
I remembered something. Dogs would
lose their trails in water. We ran through
a stream, our hearts beating faster than
ever. Then we ran into the deep, dark
woods.
'Come out, you,' said the ugly mutant.

Darmasakthini Arujunan

At The Edge Of The Cliff!

There I was, standing at the edge of the cliff,
two hundred feet above the shark-infested waters.

The ground began to crumble.
I began the long journey down - their mouths opening up ready.

I have never been so glad to be woken up for school in my entire life.

Victoria Sanders (12)

THE TOTAL ECLIPSE

As the shadow of
the great legendary
monster crept across
the land, even the
tips of the mountains
and the depths of
the valleys turned
to darkness. Flowers
closed up and animals
cowered away from
the giant. Everything
was black. Within
seconds the dazzling
sun shone back to
Earth again.

Nicola Tingle (14)

THANK GOODNESS

I looked at the broken vase,
Grandma walked in,
'My vase, who broke it?'
Grandma shouted,
'If you did I'll wash your mouth out with soap.'
Then Jake walked in and gave Grandma her
unbroken vase, 'What?' shouted Grandma,
'I made another vase just the same, it broke,'
said Jake.

Thank goodness!

Gemma Bubb (11)

UNTITLED

'Yelp, yelp,' I hear with
wonder,
I hurriedly run downstairs
and open the door.
There in front of me stands a
ferocious Alsation drooling
with blood.
There on the floor
I see my Gizmo
Head flopping and eyes
closing, I realise he's dying
'Noooooo!,' I yell
waking myself up.

Irene Davies (10)

SPIDER IN THE BATH

It sat motionless,
glaring at me, ready to get me.
Any minute now it was going to attack,
I stood there, petrified, waiting for the
battle to begin.
It started slowly moving towards me.
'Mum,' I screamed,
'There's a spider in the bath.'

Emma Jones (14)

UNDER PRESSURE

He stood extremely still. A slight smirk played around his brown lips as he tormented us with a piercing glare.
Our clammy hands anxiously fidgeted with the equipment. He had us right where he wanted - and we knew it.
'Please turn over your papers,' he snarled, 'and you may begin.'

Annabel Gaba (15)

EVIL WEARS NO FACE...

No emotion was on hers, not even the slightest
indication of empathy as she inflicted yet more pain.

The perspiration trickled down my neck. Couldn't
she see the fear on my face and the anguish
in my eyes?

She calmly stood, then announced glibly
'Stop writing and pens down please.'

Beth Winkworth (15)

TAG!

I gasped for breath,
I was exhausted!
If I ceased to escape my enemy's
clutches, I would possess a grim fate.
Reaching my destination was vital
but seemed impossible.
I decided to do all that I could do, hide!
Suddenly someone crept up behind me
and uttered 'Tag, you're it!'

Sarah Marie Jones (12)

THE MEXICAN STARING FROG

I arrived in Mexico when I
saw a sign in a shop window -
Wanted: The Mexican Staring Frog
Reward: £1000.00.
With my trap I hunted all night.
I saw it and quickly jumped up a tree.
I got my net out and caught him with it
and claimed my reward.

Alex Walpole (12)

THE MERMAID PURSE

The waves crashed onto
the rocks, while the sun
was setting in the sky,
and in the distance
something was swimming
to shore, they couldn't
tell what it was.
It swam closer
every second, they
stood stunned.
What is it? It threw
something and swam away,
it's a mermaid
purse.

Sara Jones (11)

THE RACE

Their engines roared to life,
knowing their fate if they crashed.
They were off.
The numbers reduced every time
they crossed the line . . .
40, 39, 38,
still a while to go.
An hour passes,
not knowing their fate. Then . . .
they cross the line,
Damon Hill wins the Grand Prix!

Jamie Christy (10)

THE MONSTER

Innocent-looking monster, eating away at the rocks
coming nearer and nearer. Its roar echoing from
cliff to cliff, its white mane brushing across the sand.
Keep away or you'll fall into its trap!
Splash! Glub! Too late, *yuck!* Sea water.

Angharad Heard (12)

The Forest Of No Escape

Where had I led myself? The path seemed to have faded away.
Leaves crinkled beneath my feet as I ran swiftly,
meandering through the trees that towered above my head.
Trapped in a never-ending maze.
As the pale blue sky begins to darken, I look ahead . . .
No escape!

Joanne Bamber (11)

THE MONSTER IN MY CLOSET

He just stared at me
in my closet. His eyes
were glowing in the dark,
while his fur was bulging
out like a ton of feathers.
I prepared myself for a
screaming attack, when I screamed
'Get out of my closet stupid cat!'

Emma Louise Thomas (12)

NO WAY OUT

He was surrounded by angry, vicious creatures
baying for his blood. He tried to back away.
He tried to run away. All the routes of escape
were closed off. It was the only way out.
He had no choice. He pointed to the spot.
The crowd roared.
Penalty!

Daniel O'Grady (13)

READY OR NOT

I ran as fast as I could and hid under a big
cardboard box when someone yelled 'Ready or not.'
I sat as still as I could and then I heard big
footsteps coming towards me.
Suddenly someone picked up the box and yelled
'I've found you!'

Christine Vicary (10)

TRIAL

Fear stabs like a dagger
As I sit, cold,
Alone,
Imagining the torture and interrogation that awaits.
Solemn faces swim past,
Flashing quick looks of sympathy.
I pray desperately my punishment won't be as severe
As my deadly crime . . .
The heartless voice invades my brain;
'Come in,' says the Headmaster.

Suraya Jina (16)

TOTAL ANTICIPATION

I knew it would be an unusual day.

Standing outside in the eerie cold, I felt peculiar. I sat down and waited in anticipation. The loud voice of the wind was masked by the chattering of my teeth. It was getting darker by the second.

Then, totality - total eclipse - *wow!*

Gregory Stevens (12)

A THOUSAND LETTERS!

They all stood proud then suddenly . . .
they began to tumble down one by one,
1 . . . 2 . . . 3 . . .
I picked one up, opened it, but it crumbled and fell
apart in my hands!
I placed them all back in their exact position,
so they could be read once more!
. . . The books!

Abi Anderson (12)

SHORT CHANGE

My heart began pounding and I began sweating,
he was still behind me down the dark leafy lane.
Suddenly I fell, there was jam on the trees,
butter flew everywhere. Then, big strong arms
gripped my shoulders and lifted me up.
'Rhiannon you left your change in the shop.'

Rhiannon Stanton (12)

TRAIN TRAFFIC

They sped towards each other at lightning speed.
Both geared themselves up for war.
I had seen it before.
Every second counted, but this time I felt I could do
something to prevent it.
They got closer and closer, I had to act fast.
'Switch the trains off,' I shouted.

Emily Edge (11)

NIGHTMARE

It was cold, I felt like ice was going through my body,
mist was all around me, a dark and evil laugh was
laughingly saying that he was going to kill me.
I screamed a high piercing scream, a knife was getting
closer and closer. Then I woke up.

Rhiannon Walters

NOW YOU SEE ME, NOW YOU DON'T!

I turned, there was silence, no movement.
It seemed like I was in a graveyard.
I knew they were there somewhere.
Suddenly I saw a shadowy figure run through the
edge of the woods. My heart began to pound,
 I began to sweat. Saw someone -
                    'Mob Charlie, one, two, three!'

Cerys Stanton (14)

MINI SAGA

Wham! Crash! The monster picks up the chair and
smashes it over my head. As I try to get up it squirts
hot fireballs at me. I fly backwards into the
blood-stained wall. My heart rate drops. I see the words
I dreaded to see . . . *Game over!*

Gareth Leech (12)

THE BOMB SQUAD

The bomb squad ran to the top of the warehouse,
their feet pounding against the metal stairs.
They ran at top speed. They were tired, but they
kept going. Eventually they reached the top,
but only to be greeted by the sound they feared
they would hear. *Boom!*

Dean Harris (10)

HIDE-AND-SEEK

Hiding under the big
winding staircase, it's
pitch-black. I can't see
a thing. I'm hoping that
he won't find me.
I've been hiding for what
seems ages now, not daring
to cough, sneeze, or even
breathe heavily.
'No!' I cry as my brother
opens the door shouting
          'Found you!'

Rosemary Jones (13)

THE GRAVE

As I entered the graveyard
my friend Jess yelled not
to go in.
I reached a gravestone, on it was
'Jessica died aged 12 1887-1899.
I turned around to tell Jess what I'd
found. As I turned my friend
became pale and faded before
my eyes.

Cheryl Davies (12)

BLACK CAPE COMES TO LIFE!

There he was, his sword slashing
through the air, making the room
a mess. We ran through the rooms
looking for protection.
We had found it, my room.
Suddenly it was dead silent.
We ran to my brother's room.
There lay everything *'Happy Hallowe'en'*
my brother screamed and laughed.

Rhian Thomas (12)

MAGIC CIRCLE

One wave of the wand
He overtakes her world
Her duty
She burns no more
Her fire is dimmed by his shadow
His power grows stronger, darker
Darkness now rules
She . . . is helpless
But . . .
He helps her
Bring back light
Together they create a circle,
A magic circle of light.

Emily Bethan Rees (14)

I SAW IT

I saw it.
Big and black,

Scary and dark
Huge long legs,

Furry black body
Ready for torture.

Up against the wall
Clinging on tight.

Torture coming closer;
So close - deadly!

Try to run away
But too late.

Squish - black mark on the wall,
Dead spider!

Amy Barrett (10)

THE SHARK

I'm on the beach minding my own business, when I see something. A flick of grey, a squeal, and then the sea turns red. I give a scream, there's something out there, I go to the sea to look when I'm pulled in. Goodbye, my good world of happiness, goodbye.

Angharad Rebecca Preston (10)

MAD

I hung onto a piece of rope to which was
attached a large hairy beast.
It made a loud noise that deafened me,
ran in circles
and jumped in the air.

Was every dog as excitable as mine?

Anna Blainey (11)

THE CAVE?

Wandering slowly around,
we were blindly searching for
our destination.
But then. Light! We scrambled
towards our glowing goal.
As we looked out, *aghh!*
A giant descended upon our cave.
'What are you kids doing under
the rug?'

Katherine Morgan (12)

SURVIVAL BY CHANCE

The climb had been long.
Only a few more steps to go.
Danger lurked ahead, beady eyes shining,
spitting tongue ready to strike me down.
I picked up the only thing that could save me,
I threw it.
Yes . . . a three . . . home . . . safe,
I had won.
Snakes and Ladders anyone?

Philip Dawson (10)

THE CAPTIVE

The minute he saw it he wanted it.
It called to him. He could feel his
hunger for it in the pit of his
stomach.
He leapt! He bound! Every muscle
straining to reach his destination.
He seized his captive.
'You're all mine.'
He tasted it.
'Ah . . . sweet
            chocolate
                    cake!'

Colette Morgan (13)

MONSTER CRACKER

It stood tall and proud, but I knew
that I could conquer this
individual. It had been awkward
for my friends, but it would be as
easy as pie for me, I clasped my
weapon, and, cracked that nut
open!

Johanna Rafferty (13)

THE ATTACK

They flew through the sky in their dozens,
their target was in sight. 'Get ready boys,' said
the leader. 'Get your weapons out, we're
going in.'

In they went in spirals and swirls. Would
they succeed? They did. *Ow!* 'Mum,' I shouted
'I've been stung by a wasp.'

Bethan Lewis (13)

THE THIEF

Off running was the thief who was carrying a large
bag of gold, pursued closely by the cops with
guns and dogs.

Getting tired by the minute, he felt his body failing
him.

His heart was beating like lightning.

Eventually he was caught; teeth marks sunk deep
into his legs.

Saravanan Arujunan (11)

THE ELEMENT OF SURPRISE

The sun sparkled radiantly
The waves crashed onto the shore as I
skipped merrily down to the sea
Unexpectedly, a pair of hands grasped my
waist and I was lifted into the air.
Splash!
A wave crashed over my head as I landed
with a thud in my garden pool.

Victoria Leonard (14)

THE HUNT

A few steps closer and I would have it
in my sights. The harmless creature
would be gazing down the long black
barrel that lay in my hands. I moved
closer, and pressed the trigger. The
pellets darted through the air and
hit the clay pigeon which smashed
to smithereens.

Rebecca Waite (12)

YESTERDAY'S RUBBISH

Her tongue acted like a thousand daggers
shredding my heart and reducing me to
a quivering wreck of a man as she said to me.
'I think that we were better as friends.
I don't think we should see each other anymore,'
so leaving me discarded like yesterday's rubbish!

Nicholas Like (15)

GOOD MORNING PLAYGROUP!

'Good morning Playgroup!
Today we're going to learn about music.
Now then, what's this?'
'Yes Samantha! It's a flute!
And what do we do with a flute?'
'No Jimmy, we don't eat it. That's a fruit
not a flute.
We blow into a flute.
Jimmy! That's spitting! Now sit down!
Honestly!'

Siân Harries (11)

THE ECLIPSE

The long-awaited day had arrived. Once the eclipse began I watched with my solar viewers. For ages I watched this great event, then appeared the best moment, the eclipse was full. The sight was beautiful like a golden ring, it lasted two minutes but it seemed like ten seconds.

Samantha Jones (11)

GETTING READY

He was lining up for battle,
I knew it was going
to be a tough one.
We got our weapons ready.
Our shields had to stand the
sheer force of the weapons
as they will be covered with blood.
'Oh no, it's my maths test!'
I shouted.

Darryl Ovenstone (12)

TOTAL ECLIPSE

Forcible the spherical sun shone,
Shining at me like a brutal light.
I ran to get my sunglasses.
Immediately the moon obscured the sun's surface,
leaving only the crest behind. Minutes later the
sky became palpable, everyone stood motionless,
there was silence. At that moment a flickering gleam
phosphorously glowed down on us,
the eclipse had finished.

Christina Evans (11)

THE THING IN A HOLE

She sped from room to room,
As she rapidly chased it.
No one knew what she was,
But me.

She would chase it day and night,
Just kept going, never stopping.
She aimed at my mum.
My mum screamed, *aah!*
Guess who?
It was the kitten
Chasing her torn plastic mouse.

Kirsty Gould (13)

EARTHQUAKE

Slowly, imperceptibly and like the rocking of a baby's
cradle, the Earth begins to sway. Reality strikes.
It becomes a nightmare. Buildings tumble like dominoes -
thrown forward, then back. The ground moans at its
gaping wound. Then silence. I open my eyes.
My home is gone. Only rubble remains.

Rebecca Anderson (12)

THE CHASE

I started walking
Then I ran
I was running faster and faster
I could feel my heart pounding
I was running knowing he was after me
I ran and there he was not far behind
I screamed as his hand touched my shoulder
Then he fiercely shouted 'Tag, you're it.'

Sian Griffiths (14)

THE THINGS I'LL DO FOR A FIVER!

My hand shook as I rang the doorbell.
As I entered the house I was
Attacked by the enemy.
During the gruesome battle, I
Kept one eye on the clock,
Watching the hours tick by.
The war cries were deafening.
Finally the peacemaker entered,
I had survived a night
Baby-sitting my cousins!

Siân Patrick (12)

AEROPLANE

We began travelling down the runway,
getting faster until we were no longer
on the ground. It was steady all the way.
It didn't feel like I was thirty thousand feet
up in the air. We were told to fasten our
seatbelts as we landed ready to enjoy
our holiday.

Nicola Banner-Martin (13)

FLYING

My heart pounds rapidly with
excitement as I am driven
back into my seat. I gaze
out of the miniature
window to view an enormous
mat of lush, green land.
The engine roars loudly as
I am taken further into
the everlasting sky. Yes I
am going on holiday!

Laurie Jones (12)

SHAKESPEARE IN LOVE

The two star-crossed lovers
walked in front of their awaiting crowd.
For they had waited for this time for so long.
Their hearts thumping, their minds focused on what they were doing.
This was the age old timeless story of love.
'Go on Tom, kiss her, before Miss comes back in!'

Akosa Melifonwu (13)

THE NEW VISITOR

I saw her face
So tiny and cute
She cuddled into her bed
I smiled
I could hold her in my
Arms all day long.
She was so timid.
She was quiet and strong.
I loved her with all
My heart.
I kissed my new puppy
Goodnight Rosie.

Ryan Willetts (12)

DARKNESS

There I was going fifty miles
an hour in complete darkness and
not a clue where I was heading.
Except down, and all I could hear
were screams coming from behind
me, and then I saw it. The light
shone in front of me and the ride
came to an end.

Rachel Jarvis (14)

WHEN DARKNESS FELL

It was to be an
experience of a lifetime.
Everyone gathered and prepared
for a historic event.
All the excitement had begun.
The skies went black and a
dashing light blasted from the
darkness. It was the eclipse of '99, the
whole experience was amazing.
Day became night!

Rhys Nicholas (10)

FIRST DAY

Fear lay before me.
Who would there be?
Why am I here?
Where is this place?
I leave my mother
and walk towards the door.
I let out a sigh
and my hand grabbed the handle,
I opened the door.
A smiling face beamed down upon me.
Welcome to school.

Sarah Lewis (10)

INVALID

'She's suffering from a terrible disease'
The doctors mincing voice cut through my head,
as I lay prostrate, motionless in bed.
'Skilheurtus!'
'What's that?' gasped my terrified mum.
'Thousands of kids suffer from this disease.'
The doctor paused for emphasis,
'Your daughter is suffering from
the ill-effects of Schoolitis!'

Joanne Dawkins (14)

DEATH

'Remember this, I love you like my own child.' He took one more shallow, ragged breath and squeezed Meilikki's hand. 'Go,' he whispered. His eyes flickered, then closed, his breathing stopped and he was still.

Meilikki looked one last time at the dead man. 'Goodbye Caladan,' she said softly. 'Goodbye'.

Laura Wilce (14)

A Shot At Me

He came from nowhere,
Running at me with madness in his eyes,
My legs turned to jelly,
I looked for someone to help me,
He ran until there was only 20m between him and me,
He took aim and shot,
Something whizzed past my head faster than a bullet,
Goal!

Christopher Griffiths (13)

THE DENTIST!

Feeling my stomach shaking,
It's just like the earth quaking,
Making my face go green,
It's really a sight to be seen!

After looking at my teeth,
I'm glad that's over, good grief!
What has he got to say?
Will he let me keep my teeth for today?

Just looking at the dentist,
Makes me feel like death!

Rebecca Charley (13)

LOST IN SPACE FOREVER

My rocket is on a mission
up into space,
the earth is now a tiny ball.

Getting out slowly
My cord is the only thing holding onto me,
My life depends on it.

'Snap' I fly off into space
travelling further away
I try screaming.

Phew! It was a dream.

Lucy Fowler (12)

RUGBY

Since the whistle he was as sharp as a hound after a fox.
Dodging here, there, everywhere.
'My ball,' he yelled.
'Run, run, run'
He turned to a blur.
He battled to dodge attackers,
Then . . .
Try!

Tracy Thomas (12)

Oh No Mum!

I was fighting evil princes, slaying
wicked monsters, regaining power
of castles, finding treasure, saving
villagers and catching robbers, then it
all drained away . . .
I was looking at a blank computer
screen.
'Mum! I was on level 13'
'Sorry love I had to pull the
plug, it's time for dinner!'

Julia Sandberg (11)

COLD NIGHT

It was a cold lonely night
As he lay reading in his bed
Knock, knock
He sat up in his bed trembling
'Who there?' he shouted
Knock, knock!
It came from the window
He leaped out of his bed
Grabbed his baseball bat and ran
And never returned.

Daryl Goodwin (13)

THE UNWELCOME VISITOR

In through the wide open window sneaked the silent unwanted visitor.
The visitor examined the territory.
He saw his prey and moved quickly and quietly towards it.
He stayed there frantically searching away.
Mum stood silently, weapon in hand.
'Splat, that's the end of you,' said mum to the fly.

Sarah Harris (11)

THE FRIGHTENING

I ran through the forest,
Bumping into trees and tripping over roots.
The lion was right behind me.
It leapt at me and I fell to the ground
The lion tore into me, I screamed,
I heard a voice,
'It's alright,' said my mum
'It's only a bad dream!'

Rebecca Applin (10)

MY JUNGLE

I wake up, 'Where am I? I'm in a jungle.' I look around, I see an elephant. 'Quiet, what's that?' I spot a leopard, there's a parrot flying above me, a tiger watching me through the long grass. Then I get up and clean my bedroom.

Dawn Elizabeth Emmerton (11)

WAR OF WATER

Let the battle commence. The challenge lay ahead.
There was screaming and shoving.
I was losing strength at each turn.
Our eyes met,
for a second, retreat glimmered.
With a final push my enemy plunged into
the water and a wave crashed upon me . . .
the dog was in the bath.

Michelle Langford (14)

A Journey: C'est La Vie

My life, as I knew it, was over: New existences beckoned. I found myself hurtling at a great speed through a tunnel of eternal darkness and yet, in the distance, a bright, welcoming light heralded the end.
My grandmother appeared before me . . .
'The train's slowing down. We're nearly in France!'

Michael D Brown (13)

ARACHNOPHOBIA

I looked up and there it was. Two gawping
eyes staring at me. Eight hairy legs, twitching,
just waiting to spin his trap for me. I cautiously
made my way around my predator. Suddenly
from beneath; a huge object; splodge!
Just a blooming mess where that spider
had once played.

Hannah Jenkins (14)

THE FANTASY

The boy went down
to the park.
He had a fantasy
to become a basketball player.
He started by playing
under fifteen's and got into professional basketball.
He had an accident
and it totally ruined his career.
He woke up in shock and he was sweating.

Robert Rees (10)

THE HEADMASTER'S OFFICE

I'm not usually a naughty child. So why was I
standing outside the headmaster's office? It didn't make
sense. Suddenly the door opened. A tall figure loomed in
the doorway. My heart was racing as I sat down.
'Congratulations,' he said, 'you've won first prize in
the school poetry competition!'

Lara Davies (13)

OPERATION: ENTRY

It was late. After successfully entering the building I walked down the dark passageway into an even darker room. I operated quickly and quietly, stumbling around in the darkness. Suddenly, light filled the room. My parents stood in the doorway . . . 'We told you not to go to that party!'

Michael Haddock (16)

A RESTLESS NIGHT

Aahh! Midnight is on its way.
Time for bed now, there's a storm
brewing. Crash! Is that thunder or
a vampire? Nonsense, I shake my head
and go back to sleep.
Rattle! Crash! Whoahh! I'm
not dreaming now, it's real . . . it's
the milkman. 'What a relief, breakfast
anyone?'

Jodie Parfitt (11)

THUNDERSTORM

Calm down I ordered myself. Mum will be back with some candles. Then you'll see that everything's fine. Suddenly another light flashed, I jumped, then heard the sound echoing like an earthquake, a cold wind tickled my back. Then finally I saw flames and recognised the warm flames of candles.

Arshiya Mastan (11)

THE MIDNIGHT SCARE!

It walked into my room with eyes bright red. I looked above my blanket and cried, 'Go away!' It came towards me step by step, my heart was beating fast as it gave me a kiss. I screamed and turned on the light . . . it was only my mum!

Jade Coulthard (11)

THE ENVELOPE

I waited at the letter box for the letter. Through the door it came, a bright red envelope. I opened it anxiously to see what was inside. I was delighted. I had won, I had won a million pounds. I was a millionaire at the age of twelve. Wow!

Abi Edwards (12)

THE URGING LIGHT

The light, the bright light.
Urging me, calling me.
I wanted to reach it, needed to reach it.
I was running, faster, faster, yearning!
Halt!
Something was wrong.
I was suddenly dragged away, away from
The light, screaming.
Then nothing, just darkness.
'Can you hear me darling? You're in hospital.'

Simone Morris (13)

ECLIPSE

The man had no time to loose
The eclipse was about to happen,
Everyone was nervous about the
man on the moon, there was
silence across the world.
Then before totality of the
eclipse.
The man waved to everyone he saw
on the Earth.

Andrew Butler (11)

THE LURE

I ran from school like the wind, I leaped upstairs to
my bedroom. It was calling to me, I jumped over the
gate and ran, my heart thumping like kicking a ball
100 times. The golden ground beneath me was soft,
softer than baby's skin. I just love the beach.

Bethan Jones (10)

CREEPING

Creeping! Creeping up the stairs,
footsteps unknown to me,
I listen to the sounds,
closer it gets, closer.
The landing floorboards
creak, still it gets closer,
it's shadow is vast like an
oak tree, I gasp!
'Gizmo, you silly cat, you scared me!'
Miaow.

Laura Burr (12)

SEA MONSTER

Violent waves crashed against rocks,
Sky-blue waters hide any sign of monsters
Lurking inside its cascading coral.

There's a sudden tug . . .

I pull my strong transparent line towards
me, the sun reflecting off it.
The monster emerges from the water!

'Dad, I've just caught my first fish!'

Helen Webber (12)

THE FINAL BLOW

The glittering blade fell menacingly towards my heart.

The dim mass, which was my disbelieving mind, was encircled by screaming pain as the cold steel pierced my flesh.

It effortlessly plunged through the vital beats.

Darkness overcame hysteria.

As I drew my last, agonising breath, his eyes smiled cruelly and . . .

Natasha White (15)

REVENGE

I'd been planning for weeks. Today was the day, it was her turn. My weapon was loaded - I was ready to go. The sun beat down on the concrete. I walked sneakily up behind the calm reader and shot hard. 'I'm soaked you brat!' screamed my sister. *Mission accomplished!*

Hannah Davies (12)

BURIED TREASURE

The hole where his
treasure had once been was
empty, he looked around
and there was the thief by
the field gate. He dashed
down the field. The thief
spotted him but it was too
late, Daniel leaped onto
his back, retrieved his
bone, lay down and ate it.

Ben Hebblewhite (14)

11TH OF AUGUST 1999, A HISTORIC DAY, AN ECLIPSE AND I WROTE THIS MINI SAGA

Darkness fell upon me, there was no light, I looked at my bedside clock, and the date read 11/08/99, the time 11:11 am, that's strange, I thought, I looked out through my window, up at the sun, it was black in the middle and light around the sides. The Eclipse.

Dafydd Jones (14)

THE BLACK MONSTER

As I raced down the street, I glimpsed a huge black monster behind me. I had to get away, I headed towards the disused factory, too late - I could feel it getting nearer, suddenly I felt it lick my leg, when I turned it was a big black *labrador*.

Christopher Williams (11)

THE RACING PIGEON

Watching, waiting, scanning the skies
With hopeful eyes.
Looking for a dot on the horizon.
Heart beating, clock ticking,
Corn tin shaking in his hand.
'Come on, come on!' he cries.
A flutter of feathers,
flies into the loft,
off with the rubber
and into the clock.

Emma O'Connell (10)

THE MOON THAT NEEDED A FRIEND

I was tucked inside my bed when I thought the moon was calling me. It was, the moon was really calling me. He told me that he had no friends in space. He needed someone to be his friend and keep him company every night from this day on and for ever.

Moshudul Islam (11)

THE STALKER

I ran faster than ever before knowing that I was being followed. I couldn't carry on running anymore. My adrenaline pumped faster. Closer and closer he came, then suddenly a hand appeared from behind me. *'Tag, you're it,'* and the chase was on again!

Jade Wood (13)

THE FIRST

The crowd moved forward. I could feel my heart pounding in my chest. I had to keep running. The sweat was running down my face but still I kept running. And there it was looming in front of me. I had to be one of the first on the Nemesis.

Leanne Gardner (13)

TIME IS PRECIOUS

The irony, all the while he is gone, every second, slowly counted, yet the minutes that mattered most, so unaware, were dangerously ticking by.

She painfully regretted every second she spent without him, and the wasted hours of arguing, and hating him for things that simply annoyed her.

Time is precious.

Charlotte Allen (16)

TEMPTATION

There was a fork in the path.
One way was marked *Good,* the other, *Evil.*
Good was rocky and steep. *Evil* was broad and pleasant.
I called upon all my reserves of strength.
A battle raged in my inner self.
Good won.
I put the chocolate back in the cupboard.

Manuela Solera-Deuchar (14)

I SURRENDER

I screamed. Held my hands high above my head.

It was getting scary now, all life drained out of me. Everything went black.
'I surrender!' I shouted but it was too loud, no one heard. I screamed.

The roller-coaster screeched to a halt. I sat motionless, breathless.

Rebecca Tudgay (13)

EARTH WARS

I drew my weapon and prepared for battle. My opponent was tall, frightening, he made me feel ominous. I felt sick inside, but I had to fight him. He edged closer taunting me as he came. I felt my heart race. He struck as I fell to the floor dead.

Shaun Jennings (11)

FEAR AND TRIUMPH

He's wrenched mercilessly from the soft pillows of his bed and forced into a dark tunnel, allowed only moments of rest before he's forced onwards. He surfaces at last from the dark into a glaring light as his mother looks lovingly into her newborn son's eyes.

Becky Hammonds (16)

SPACE - THE ONE AND ONLY VOYAGE TO MARS

As the craft came close to the destination of Mars the fiery red planet was upon them. As they got close to the burning planet they became so hot they thought they were chickens in an oven. The ship landed, the crew took three steps each as the planet disappeared.

Rachael Fretwell (12)

THE ECLIPSE

The children were still
running away from
the darkness.
All the other people
shouted and cried.
'It's a once in
a lifetime chance
of seeing the black
wonder.' The darkness
covered us like a
rolling boulder.
The excitement burned
up inside. Then the
brightness came back
and startled me
very much.

Elinor Marsh (13)

IT CAME AND IT WENT

There it was,
Black, everything black,
except for a rim of orange.
We couldn't see anything . . .

The darkness lasted for 1-2 minutes,
then the daylight started to come
through . . .

It started to become light,
with a little chill and a bit
of a breeze,
it vanished,
gone . . .

Andrea Roberts (15)

WHERE'S THE EXIT?

It felt like a matter of life or death. I was trapped and I didn't know which way to turn. I was surrounded by green and up above me it was blue. Suddenly I saw the exit. I ran to it and saw a sign saying 'Maze Exit.'

Sarah Davies (12)

NEWCOMER

We were all very excited. My dad made up the small bed. Me and my brother brought the special food. My mum rested with her feet up. We all waited for the day to arrive. My mum drove home with the newcomer. We all welcomed Flyn our new dog.

Sam Brown (11)

SILENT DARKNESS

Passing the window. Adrenaline rush. Pacing faster, looking out of the window not staring at it. Darkness begins filling the sky, pupils dilating. Waiting anxiously. Clutching the curtains, nose pressed against the glass. Alone in the silence shivering, thinking of fear. Eyes rapidly following the black quilt mysteriously, motionless. Totality.

Nicole Bruton (14)

THE TRIAL

As I stepped into the dock, I knew the extent of my crime. I was guilty and should be punished. My mother wept. The accusing eyes of the judge and jury bore into me as I voiced my plea.

The verdict - guilty.

The sentence - 'You're grounded!' stormed my father.

Sharon Davies (15)

DIAMOND

The first contact reached us. All the people in my village looked up with their filtered glasses and champagne glass and enjoyed a once in a lifetime event. Suddenly it all went dark and the flashing of cameras brightened the sky. In two minutes the amazing diamond corona had gone.

Hannah Aylward (12)

A PLOT TO KILL

I heard the car creeping up behind me. I turned and was met by the barrel of a gun. I heard a loud bang piercing the air and a sharp pain in my chest. As I fell to the ground I saw a black Mercedes drive off into the distance.

Sara Brunt (13)

THE TIGER

He was lying in the tall grass, waiting to pounce on the unsuspecting antelope, grazing on the open plain.

'Hey! Is the camera rolling?' asked the director, for they were filming this.

Then, suddenly, he pounced and ran.

The antelope ran as fast as the lightning that struck the tree.

Freya Michaud (10)

THE NAPPY ARGUMENT

We argued for hours, I wasn't doing it, why should I change Kyle's nappy when I do it all the time.

I screamed at her, so she screamed back. Then Mum walked in and caught her screaming. So she had to change Kyle's nappy. I laughed and walked away. Ha!

Katrina Sweetser-Hawkes (11)

A SPOOKY NIGHT

There was a chilly wind outside
The back door was not shut
So it kept banging to the beat of my heart
Then a howl sent shivers down my spine
The door banged faster like my pulse
Then another howl reminded me
That my dog had not been fed!

Phillip J Lewis (12)

THE SCREAMING WOLF

We were playing in the park. We heard something screaming. We looked, it was a screaming wolf from the story our brother told us. We ran around the park, he went to eat me and Ben. I heard more screaming, it was my screaming werewolf alarm clock.

Ashley Bolwell (11)

HIDDEN

The pound of their footfalls echoed through the air. She stepped back fearfully, into the hanging shadows of the tall Victorian houses. The cool wall collided with her back, the dampness seeping through her clothes. Her heart thumped as they approached her hiding place . . .
'Ha, I found you, you're *it!*'

Adele Watts (12)

TIME TO TOTALITY

At first there was just a small chunk missing, then came the grin of the Cheshire cat smiling down as the sun was swallowed by darkness. A halo of light shone from the sky, the air was cool, as the end of totality neared, and once more the sun blazed.

Helen Jennifer Jones (14)

MY MUM

My mum is so special,
She cares for me,
I love my mum,
I'm her lovely son.

She makes me dinner,
She takes me out,
She washes my clothes,
That's her.

She's always with me,
She is, she is,
That is my mum,
It is, it is.

Nilesh Mepani (12)

NIGHTMARE!

The white Micra raced up the road. It reversed up the driveway knocking over the dustbin and almost hitting the cat! The front door swung open. The nightmare had begun! She raced through the hall with her glasses on and teeth clicking.

Gran had come to stay!

Bernadette Lemon (13)

THE GUSH IN THE WIND

It was a pale but very windy afternoon
the wind had started to lose its little blows
it started a twirl in the distance
what could that be, thought I, a tornado maybe?
'Mam, Dad,' I cried, 'come quick, it's a tornado in the distance.'
'You're quite right son, it is. Run!'

Nick Taylor (11)

GAME OVER

It was game over for me.

That's what he said in a deep loud voice anyway.

It was suddenly impossible to see anything other than the words
'Game Over'.

I tried closing my eyes and opening them again.

Where am I? . . . 'Hey bro, you died, it's my go on the computer now!'

Derek Pang (14)

THE ECLIPSE

Today we will witness the talked about eclipse.

The daylight fades as an eerie night sky takes centre stage. I stand and watch the last golden beam disappear. Totality takes place, what an outstanding, unbelievable sight we have seen.

Its audience stand gobsmacked at this magical event.

Clare Sim (12)

THE IMPORTANT DOCUMENT

I sat on the chair as the dreaded moment approached.
He reached out his hand for the document. 'Where is it?' he shouted.
'I'll give you one last chance!'
Then I answered in a low whisper: 'The homework's in my bag, sir.'

Lowri Evans (12)

A Golden Silence

The silver needle pierced through the back of her skinny neck. Her vision became a blur of purple, black, and red. Her head began to drop with her long golden hair pulling her down. Her brain switched off and she slowly fell to the floor holding the suicide weapon.

Caroline McBurnie Jones (14)

IN THE MIDDLE OF THE NIGHT

In the middle of the night I was sleeping in my bed when I saw a monster with four eyes and three legs. I screamed as he came towards me. He took hold of me and started shaking me. Just then I woke up and my mother was shaking me . . .

Joanna Moore (12)

HILDA'S BIG TRICK

Hilda was a witch. She was easily embarrassed, typically she was nominated to perform a big trick.

When she got home, she practised immediately because she didn't want to be laughed at in the show.

That night she performed her trick with dignity, she turned herself into every single element.

Kayleigh Baldwin (12)

OH! BROTHER

He walks into my room as if he was innocent of all charges.
'Get out,' I shout 'you horrible little boy.'
He just sits and ignores me like a deaf person who is evil looking.
When finally my brother shouted 'No' and ran out of my room.
'Yes, at last.'

Emma Louise Bates (12)

A RAY OF LIGHT

Darkness spread over the land, everyone grew silent. The expressions changed as night drew. A burst of light blinded the watch people, they stood fixed. Adrenaline rushed as you saw outlines of faces and scenery. The moment of totality came, the sparkling diamond ring showed herself - it was an eclipse.

Chantelle Thomas (15)

Today's The Day!

It's dark outside
Oh, so quiet
But listen - can you hear it?
Footsteps on the stairs,
It's getting closer,
Closer still,
My stomach churns,
My heart races,
The bedroom door opens,
Then, it's upon me!
Oh! No!
Morning, darling
Time to get up!
High school begins today
Phew! Oh Mum.

Lucy Jayne Marsh (11)

THE SORRY HUNTER

The feline stalks her prey,
watching its every moment from a pair
of beady, ready eyes. She breathes quietly,
moving with ease and silence.
Then she jumps and with two threatening paws,
lunges her lethal claws towards the victim.
She regrets ever sticking her claws into her own tail.

Lisa Francis (14)

THE CHASE

I run as fast as I can around and around as he chases me
I throw the ball, he shoots to catch it.
He catches it. I call him, he barks and comes to me.
He drops the ball and I pick it up and the chase starts all over again.

Rhiannon Sheppard (10)